S0-ADS-297

a Buddha to be.   *–unknown*

Beauty is eternity gazing at itself in a mirror.

-Kahlil Gibran

JEWEL OF THE LOTUS

an illustrated journal

When you
touch a body,
you touch
the whole
person,
the intellect,
the spirit,
and
the emotions.

-Jane Harrington

The lotus
is a symbol
of purity.
Its roots are
in the mud,
but the flower
remains above
the dirty water.

Live the lotus life.

Be in the world,
but unaffected
by impurities.

–Innerspace

The foundations of the world are to be found, not in the cognitive experience of conscious thought, but in the aesthetic experience of everyday life.

-Alfted North Whitehead

In all things of nature there is something marvelous.   *-Aristotle*

| rest

in the

grace

of the

world,

and am

free.

–Wendell Berry

Enlightenment

is just

another word

for feeling

comfortable

with being

a completely

ordinary

person.

-Veronique Vienne

Nature holds
the key
to our
aesthetic,
intellectual,
cognitive
and even
spiritual
satisfaction.

-Edward O. Wilson

∫pirituality

is like a bird:

If you hold it

too closely,

it chokes,

And if

you hold it

too loosely,

it escapes.

–Israel Salanter Lipkin

You can search the whole universe
and not find a single being
more worthy of love than yourself.

-Buddha

It takes two to speak the truth, one to speak, and another to hear.   *-Thoreau*

The world is magic
when your eyes are open
to the love and beauty
inherent in every moment.

-Sophie Morris

The Beauty
of Life
surrounds me,
the Joy
of Life
uplifts me,
and the
Resilience
of Life
protects me.
It is enough.

–Laura Teresa Marquez

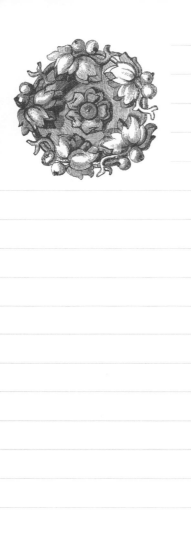

Beauty is
eternity
gazing
at itself
in the
mirror.

-Kahlil Gibran

*S*erenity is not freedom from the storm but peace within the storm.   *–unknown*

Walk slowly and bow often. *-Mary Oliver*

Philosophy is
harmonized
knowledge
making a
harmonious life;
it is the self-discipline
which lifts us
to serenity
and freedom.

Knowledge
is power,
but only
wisdom
is liberty.

-Will Durant

Calmness comes
from within.
It is the peace
and restfulness
of the depths
of our nature.

The fury
of storm
and of wind
agitate only
the surface
of the sea;
they penetrate
only two or
three hundred feet;
below that
is the calm,
unruffled deep.

To be ready
for the great
crises of life
we must learn
serenity
in our daily living.

Calmness is
the crown
of self-control.

-William Jordan

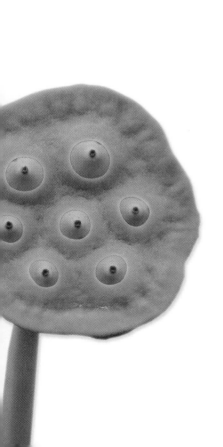

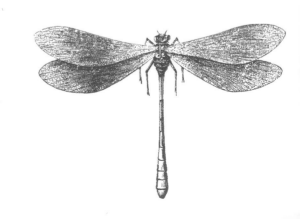

When the soul looks out of its body, it should only see beauty in its path . . .   *-Yusef Lateef*

The serenity of mind, gentleness, silence, self-restraint,

and the purity of mind are called the austerity of thought. *-Bhagavad Gita*

And the day came
when the risk
to remain in a
tight bud was more
painful
than the risk it took
to bloom.

-Anais Nin

Dance is life.
Stillness
is love.
Together,
they are
everything.

-Debbie Nargi-Brown

Rare is the union of beauty and purity.   *–Juvenal*

Aspire. Renounce. Meditate. Be good; do good.

Be kind; be compassionate. Inquire, know thyself.   *-Swami Sivinada*

Look to this day, for it is Life, the very life of Life;

in its brief course lie all the verities

and realities of your existence… *-Kalidasa*

The bliss of Growth,
the glory of Action,
the splendor of Beauty.

For Yesterday is but a
dream, And Tomorrow
only a vision;

But Today well lived makes
Yesterday a dream of
Happiness.

And Tomorrow
a vision of Hope.

Look well, therefore,
to this day.

Such is the salutation to
the dawn.

-Kalidasa

A lotus for you, a Buddha to be. *-unknown*

The moment
of enlightenment
is when a
person's dreams
of possibilities
become images
of probabilities.

-V.C. Braden

JEWEL OF THE LOTUS

an illustrated journal

The Lotus rises from the calm depths of water, drawn by light,
emerging as a stunning jewel. Revered for centuries, the auspicious lotus
symbolizes beauty, purity and enlightenment.

Copyright © 2008. Published by Brush Dance
All rights reserved.

No part of this book may be reproduced or transmitted in any form
or by any means, electronic or mechanical, including photocopying,
recording, or by any information storage and retrieval system,
without written permission from the publisher.

Book design by Liz Kalloch